English Skills

© 2006 Folens Limited, on behalf of the author.

United Kingdom: Folens Publishers, Waterslade House, Thame Road, Haddenham, Buckinghamshire, HP17 8NT
Email: folens@folens.com

Ireland: Folens Publishers, Greenhills Road, Tallaght, Dublin 24
Email: info@folens.ie

Editor: Geraldine Sowerby
Layout artist: Patricia Hollingsworth
Illustrations: Tony Randall
Cover design: Martin Cross
Editorial consultant: Helen Whittaker

First published 2006 by Folens Limited.

Every effort has been made to contact copyright holders of material used in this publication. If any copyright holder has been overlooked, we should be pleased to make any necessary arrangements.

British Library Cataloguing in Publication Data. A catalogue record for this publication is available from the British Library.

ISBN 978 1 84303 853 5

Contents

A **Read about our world. Colour the pictures.**

Our World

We live on a planet called Earth. The Earth is round, like a ball. It is one of nine planets which move around the Sun. The path each planet takes around the Sun is called its orbit. The Sun and the planets together are called the Solar System. The Earth is the only planet in the Solar System which has living things.

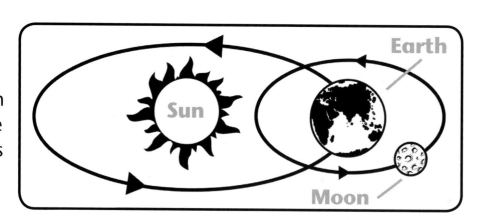

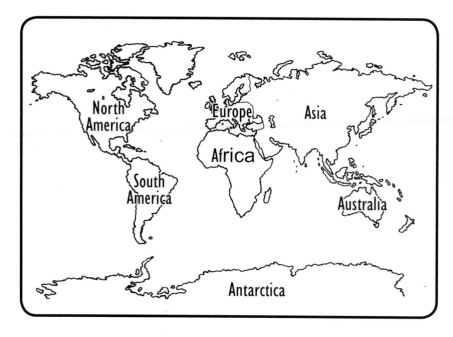

Most of the surface of the Earth is covered in water. The largest pieces of land are called continents. There are seven continents. They are Africa, Antarctica, Asia, Australia, Europe, North America and South America. Can you find them all on the map? Do you live on one of them?

Some places on Earth are flat and some have mountains. Some places are hot and some are cold. Some places have lots of rain and some are very dry. Some places are near the sea and some are inland. What is it like where you live?

A Write yes or no.

1. We live on a planet called Mars. _____

2. There are nine planets in the Solar System. _____

3. The Earth is the only planet in the Solar
   System with life. _____

4. Most of the Earth's surface is land. _____

5. The largest pieces of land are called islands. _____

6. There are seven continents. _____

B Unscramble these sentences.

1. is continent a Europe.

   _____

2. live on We Earth.

   _____

3. places Some lots of have rain.

   _____

C Choose the correct word.

1. The Earth is a _____. (continent, orbit, planet)

2. There are nine planets which move around the _____.
   (Sun, Earth, Moon)

3. The Earth's path around the Sun is called its _____.
   (continent, orbit, planet)

4. Africa is a _____. (continent, orbit, planet)

5. There are _____ (many, seven, nine) continents.

6. You can find the continents on a _____.
   (mat, map, man)

© Folens (copiable page)   English Skills 2   **5**

A Write the correct initial letter (a, e, i, o, u).

B Write the correct initial letter.

English Skills 2

Capital Letters

We use a capital letter at the beginning of a sentence.
Examples: It is a cold day. Meg has a new coat.

 Write these sentences correctly.

1. the bear is brown.

_____

2. yasmin has a new red bike.

_____

3. an old tree fell down.

_____

4. a bee stung me.

_____

5. tom likes doing homework.

_____

 Unscramble these sentences Add capital letters.

1. the tall fell man.

_____

2. fish the orange is.

_____

3. kitten my is lovely.

_____

4. house my in is town.

_____

5. books ben reading loves.

_____

Activities

A **Write about yourself.**

1. My name is _____ .

2. I am _____ years old.

3. I have _____ eyes.

4. I have _____ hair.

5. I live in _____ .

6. I have _____ brother(s).

7. I have _____ sister(s).

8. The name of my school is _____ .

9. I am in _____ class.

10. There are _____ children in my class.

11. My teacher's name is _____ .

12. My favourite colour is _____ .

13. My friends are called _____ .

14. The things I like doing are: _____

_____ .

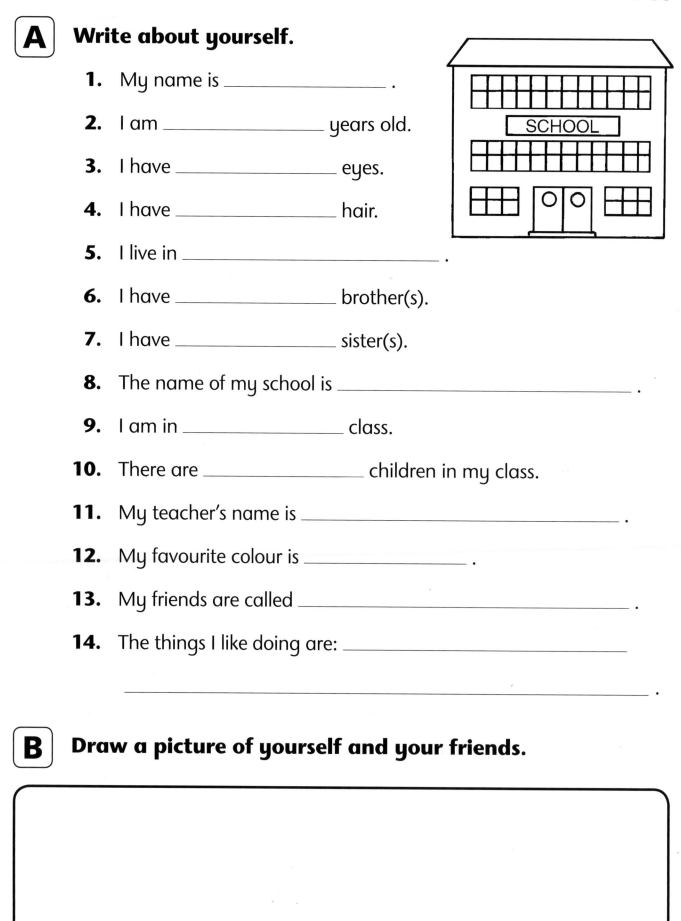

B **Draw a picture of yourself and your friends.**

> **Choose the group name.**
> **Example: Monday, Friday, Sunday. The group name is days.**

A flowers birds fruit seasons animals places clothes drinks

1. spring, summer, winter   _____

2. apple, orange, banana   _____

3. skirt, dress, shirt   _____

4. robin, chicken, blackbird   _____

5. Africa, Japan, Bogotá   _____

6. fox, squirrel, rabbit   _____

7. tea, coffee, milk   _____

8. tulip, daffodil, daisy   _____

B **Write the missing words.**

| live | Earth | dry | covered | Solar |
| hot | planet | some | lots | mountains |

We _____ on Earth. It is the only _____ in the _____ System which has life. Most of the Earth is _____ by ocean. Some places on _____ are flat and some have _____ . Some places are _____ and some are cold. Some places have _____ of rain and _____ are very _____ .

C **Unscramble these letters.**

1. odlc   _____   **4.** rtahE   _____

2. anir   _____   **5.** atenlp   _____

3. saiA   _____   **6.** coane   _____

Read about swallows. Colour the picture.

Swallows

Swallows have long, pointed wings and a forked tail. A swallow's back is covered in shiny, dark-blue feathers. The feathers on its chest and underneath its wings are white or cream. Its throat is red.

Swallows live in gardens, marshes, moors and fields. Swallows eat insects which they catch in the air. They build nests on ledges in barns and sheds. The bowl-shaped nest is built from mud and grass, and is lined with soft feathers and hair. The female swallow lays between four and six eggs. She sits on them for about two weeks. While she sits on the eggs, the male swallow feeds her. When the eggs have hatched, the young birds are fed by both parents.

Swallows live in Europe during spring and summer, from April to September. In September they flock together in big groups and fly to Africa. They spend the winter in Africa, where it is much warmer and there is plenty of food. In the spring they fly north again.

A **Answer these questions using complete sentences.**

1. Where do swallows live?

_____

2. What do swallows eat?

_____

3. How many eggs does a female swallow lay?

_____

4. Who are the young birds fed by?

_____

5. Where do swallows live during spring and summer?

_____

6. Where do swallows spend the winter?

_____

 B **Label each picture. Colour them in.**

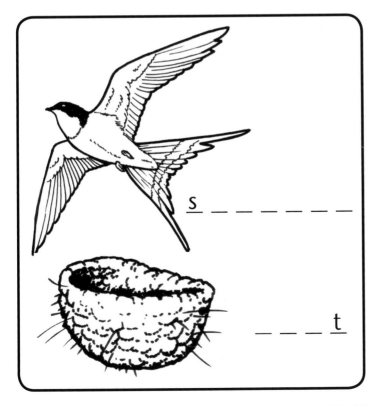

s _ _ _ _ _ _

_ _ _ _ t

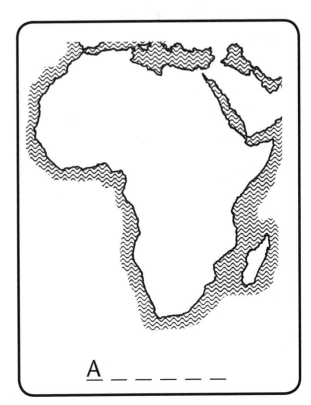

A _ _ _ _ _ _

Dec '11

A Choose the correct missing letter (a, e, i, o, u).

n__t	p__n	b__n	b__t
r__d	m__p	m__t	c__t
d__g	n__t	l__g	f__n
s__n	b__s	p__n	p__g

B Ring the correct word.

pull (pill)	dull doll	duck luck	bill bell
hall hill	rack rock	well will	lock luck
suck sack	beg bed	bad bag	tap tan

Dec '11

> **We use a capital letter for the names of people.**
> **Example: Ben gave Sam an apple.**

 A **Write these sentences correctly.**

1. mansa and femi are twins.

_____

2. My friend's name is emma.

_____

3. baldev goes fishing with prasad.

_____

4. the teacher gave ken and pam a star.

_____

5. kim got an orange and kate got a banana.

_____

6. rani is taller than badra.

_____

 B **Unscramble these sentences.**
Do not forget capital letters!

1. likes ben dogs and likes jim cats.

_____

2. hedgehog henry the asleep is.

_____

3. playing zindel is lantz with.

_____

4. smaller sally is sam than.

_____

Writing

 A **Write two sentences for each picture. Use the help words.**

My Birthday

	postman parcel card **1.** _____ _____ **2.** _____ _____
	opened money book **1.** _____ _____ **2.** _____ _____
	friends party games **1.** _____ _____ **2.** _____ _____
	blew candles sang **1.** _____ _____ **2.** _____ _____

14 English Skills 2 © Folens (copiable page)

A **Choose the 'group name'.**

birds trees fruit flowers dogs vegetables animals fish

1. rose, buttercup, snowdrop _____

2. oak, beech, horse chestnut _____

3. plum, apple, orange _____

4. trout, salmon, cod _____

5. lion, elephant, monkey _____

6. boxer, greyhound, poodle _____

7. robin, magpie, crow _____

8. carrot, turnip, cabbage _____

B **Choose the correct word.**

fur feathers scales wool shell thick skin

1. A fish has a covering of _____ .

2. A sheep has a covering of _____ .

3. A swallow has a covering of _____ .

4. A squirrel has a covering of _____ .

5. A crab has a covering of _____ .

6. An elephant has a covering of _____ .

C **Choose the missing words.**

hatched feathers eggs parents nests birds two

Swallows build their _____ from mud and grass, and line them with soft _____ and hair. The female swallow lays between four and six _____ . She sits on them for about _____ weeks. When the eggs have _____ , the young _____ are fed by both _____ .

Read the story. Colour the picture.

The Playful Puppy

Pam's [puppy] chased after a [stick] hat Pam threw. The [stick] with

a splash into a [pond] and the little [puppy] jumped in after it.

A [duck] quacked and swam behind a [log] The stick landed near

some [flowers] : puppy grabbed the stick. He dropped it at

Pam's [boots] . He splashed her [legs] is he shook himself dry. A [horse]

looked over an old [gate] and the [puppy] barked at it. Pam held the playful

puppy by the [collar] . She led it up the [path] and home for tea.

A **Answer these questions.**

1. What is the name of the story?

_____

2. What did Pam throw?

_____

3. What did the duck do?

_____

4. Where did the stick land?

_____

5. What did the puppy bark at?

_____

6. How did Pam hold the puppy?

_____

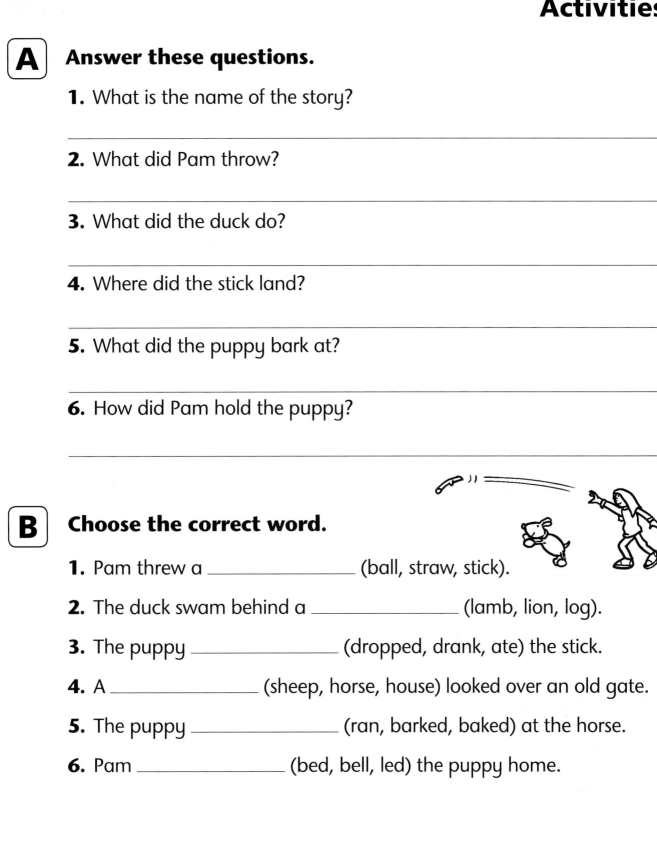

B **Choose the correct word.**

1. Pam threw a _____ (ball, straw, stick).

2. The duck swam behind a _____ (lamb, lion, log).

3. The puppy _____ (dropped, drank, ate) the stick.

4. A _____ (sheep, horse, house) looked over an old gate.

5. The puppy _____ (ran, barked, baked) at the horse.

6. Pam _____ (bed, bell, led) the puppy home.

C **Unscramble these letters.**

1. pyupp _____

2. spshla _____

3. ickst _____

4. ydr _____

5. edbark _____

6. mohe _____

A **Write the missing letters.**

st   fl   gl   sw   cr   br

__ __ ag   __ __ ab   __ __ ag

__ __ im   __ __ ass   __ __ ick

B **Ring the correct initial sounds.**

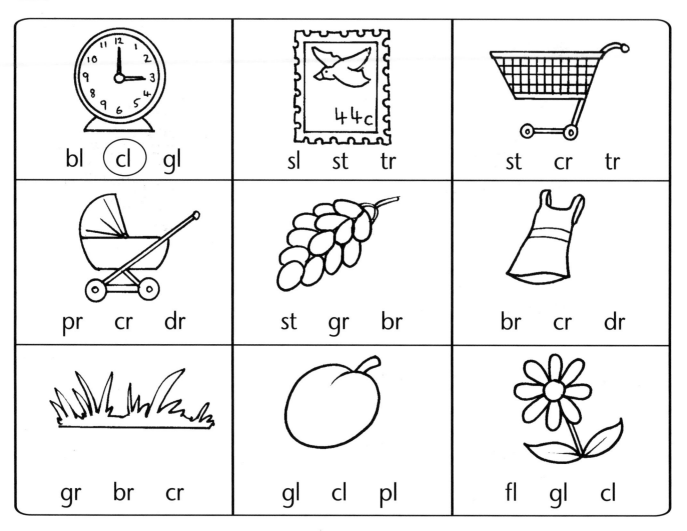

bl (cl) gl   sl st tr   st cr tr

pr cr dr   st gr br   br cr dr

gr br cr   gl cl pl   fl gl cl

> We use a capital letter for the word I.
> Example: I like my school.

A **Write these sentences correctly.**

1. Meera and i were going to the party.

_____

2. i wish i was going to the party.

_____

3. i said i was sick.

_____

4. i like apples but i prefer bananas.

_____

5. i wish i could sing the song.

_____

6. Dad said i could go so i am going.

_____

B **Unscramble these sentences.**
Do not forget capital letters!

1. landed an alien i and saw it.

_____

2. said i was i home going.

_____

3. and tom i going are swimming.

_____

4. the i read book and i it loved.

_____

Write two sentences for each picture. Use the help words.

A Visit to the Zoo

family   bus   paid   tickets

1. _____

_____

2. _____

_____

monkeys   cage   swinging   laughed

1. _____

_____

2. _____

_____

lion   roared   hid   scared

1. _____

_____

2. _____

_____

seals   fish   bucket   jumped

1. _____

_____

2. _____

_____

A **Choose the correct word.**

1. A dog has a coat of _____. (wool, feathers, fur)

2. A dog's house is called a _____. (hutch, kennel, nest)

3. A baby dog is called a _____. (cub, kid, puppy)

4. A happy dog wags its _____. (ear, tail, head)

5. An angry dog _____. (yells, growls, hops)

6. A dog has four _____. (eyes, tails, paws)

B **Choose the missing words. Colour the picture.**

chased	home	stung	bee
tulip	nose	butterfly	puppy

The playful _____ chased a _____ into a

flowerbed. He stuck his _____ into a _____ .

An angry _____ flew out. The bee _____ the

puppy on the nose. The puppy ran _____ . He never

_____ a butterfly again!

A **Read the story. Colour the picture.**

The Pine Tree

A little pine tree was very unhappy. "I hate having green needles," said the little tree. "I wish I had leaves of gold."

A very kind fairy heard the pine tree. She waved her magic wand and the little tree got leaves of gold!

However, a robber came by and saw the golden leaves. "Ha! Ha!" he said. "I have found gold." He picked all the leaves and soon the little pine tree was bare. "Maybe glass leaves would be better," thought the little tree. So the little fairy waved her magic wand and the pine tree got leaves of glass.

However, as soon as the wind began to blow, all the glass leaves got broken. Once again the pine tree was bare. "I wish I had green leaves," grumbled the tree. The kind fairy gave the tree green leaves and for a while the tree was happy.

However, soon a goat came along. "What juicy leaves," he said, "and I can reach every leaf!" The hungry goat ate every single leaf on the tree. Once again the pine tree was bare.

"Oh dear! Oh dear!" cried the tree. "Green leaves are fine for big trees, but I wish I could have my needles back. Robbers do not steal them, the wind will not break them and goats will not eat them."

Next morning, her needles were back. "These are the best kind of leaves," laughed the little tree and she was never unhappy again.

A **Answer these questions.**

1. Who heard the pine tree's wish?

_____

2. Who picked all the golden leaves?

_____

3. What happened to the glass leaves?

_____

4. What happened to the green leaves?

_____

5. Was the pine tree big or small?

_____

6. Was the pine tree happy in the end?

_____

B **Choose the correct name for each leaf.**

oak   holly   chestnut   beech   ash

h_____   a_____   c_____   b_____   o_____

C **Unscramble these letters.**

1. seaelv   _____   **4.** toga   _____

2. sslga   _____   **5.** yiafr   _____

3. dlog   _____   **6.** reborb   _____

A Ring the correct word.

(bunk) bank	dust dump	bend belt	bump pump
hunt hump	belt desk	milk mist	sulk sunk
damp bank	jump bump	test tusk	sulk risk

B Ring the correct final sounds.

lp (lt) ld	nd lt nt	ld mp nd
st sk sp	st lt sk	st nd nk

Capital Letters

> We use capital letters for the names of places.
> Example: Moscow is the capital of Russia.

A **Write these sentences correctly.**

1. The ship sailed from new york to london.

_____

2. The capital of france is paris.

_____

3. Rice is grown in india and china.

_____

4. The jet landed at singapore airport.

_____

5. The train is going to lima and then la paz.

_____

6. I have a cousin in mumbai and an uncle in karachi.

_____

B **Try this capital cities wordsearch.**

Ottawa   Rome

Cairo   Accra

Pretoria   Canberra

Riyadh   Rabat

Delhi   Brasilia

a	C	O	t	t	a	w	a
C	a	i	r	o	g	i	h
R	n	h	D	e	l	h	i
o	b	e	d	i	g	e	t
m	e	n	s	a	f	o	a
e	r	a	k	l	y	m	b
P	r	e	t	o	r	i	a
B	a	A	c	c	r	a	R

Writing

A | **Write three sentences for each picture. Use the help words.**

The Tyre Swing

tyre   swing   tree   rope

1. _____

_____

2. _____

_____

3. _____

_____

pond   splash   accident   worried

1. _____

_____

2. _____

_____

3. _____

_____

boat   fun   paddle

1. _____

_____

2. _____

_____

3. _____

_____

A Write by or buy.

1. I have to _____ a new copy.

2. John, are you going _____ the school?

3. I don't have the money to _____ sweets.

4. The bus went _____ the bus stop.

5. Where can you _____ a newspaper?

6. The book was written _____ Lin Yung.

7. The rabbit ran _____ the fox.

8. The picture was painted _____ Deepak Patel.

B Write the missing words.

green   broken   fairy   glass   robber   morning
leaves   happy   gold   tree   needles

A little pine tree didn't like her green _____ . She wished

for leaves of _____ . A fairy gave her _____ of gold

but a _____ stole them. The pine tree wished for leaves of

_____ . The _____ gave her leaves of glass but they got

_____ . The pine _____ wished for _____ leaves

but a goat ate them. The pine tree wished for her own needles again.

Next _____ , her needles were back. The pine tree was now

_____ .

C Write yes or no.

1. The fairy was a kind fairy.   _____

2. A robber ate the golden leaves.   _____

3. The robber broke the glass leaves.   _____

4. A goat ate the green leaves.   _____

A **Read the story. Colour the picture.**

At the Zoo

Meg and Tom are at the [ZOO] Here are some [monkeys]. Monkeys love

to eat [bananas]. One monkey is cheeky. He pulls a [feather] of a lady's [hat]

. A zookeeper with big [boots] tells him to give it back. The children can see

an [elephant] eating an [apple]. She uses her [trunk] to put it into her mouth.

Here comes a [camel] along the [path]. What a big hump it has! Now look

at the [giraffe]. It has a long [neck] and [spots] all over its body. Meg and Tom

go to see the [snakes]. Then they go to see the [lions]. Meg and Tom

love the zoo.

English Skills 2

A **Write yes or no.**

1. Meg and Tom are at the library. _____

2. Monkeys love to eat bananas. _____

3. The zookeeper has big gloves. _____

4. The elephant used her trunk to eat a burger. _____

5. The camel has a hump. _____

6. The giraffe has stripes all over its body. _____

B **Answer these questions in full sentences.**

1. Where are Tom and Meg?

_____

2. What did one monkey do?

_____

3. What was the elephant doing?

_____

4. What kind of neck does a giraffe have?

_____

5. What was the last animal Meg and Tom saw?

_____

6. What do Meg and Tom think of the zoo?

_____

C **Unscramble these letters.**

1. keymon _____ **4.** thmou _____

2. erkeepzoo _____ **5.** mphu _____

3. renildch _____ **6.** dybo _____

A **Make word families.**

– ing

_r_ ing

___ ing

___ ing

___ ing

– ck

_r_ _o_ ck

___ ___ ck

___ ___ ck

___ ___ ck

– ll

_h_ _i_ ll

___ ___ ll

___ ___ ll

___ ___ ll

– all

_h_ all

___ all

___ all

___ all

– old

_h_ old

___ old

___ old

___ old

– y

_b_ _a_ _b_ y

___ ___ ___ y

___ ___ y

___ ___ ___ y

Capital Letters

> **We use a capital letter for week days, months and special days.**
> **Examples: Tuesday, May, New Year's Day.**

Write these sentences correctly.

1. new year's day is in january.

_____

2. may comes between april and june.

_____

3. my birthday is on tuesday this year.

_____

4. I will be away from february to july.

_____

5. april fool's day is on friday this year.

_____

6. we are going on holiday on the first wednesday in november.

_____

B **Circle the words which should always have a capital letter.**

day   thursday   spring   april   festival

eid   christmas   diwali

Write two sentences for each picture. Use the help words.

A Fall of Snow

	snow deep robin hungry
	1. _____
	_____
	2. _____
	_____
	snowman garden scarf
	1. _____
	_____
	2. _____
	_____
	snowballs threw friend
	1. _____
	_____
	2. _____
	_____
	sunshine melted ground
	1. _____
	_____
	2. _____
	_____

A **Choose the correct word.**

nest   burrow   run   kennel   den   stable

1. A dog lives in a _____ .

2. A chicken lives in a _____ .

3. A fox lives in a _____ .

4. A horse lives in a _____ .

5. A rabbit lives in a _____ .

6. A wasp lives in a _____ .

B **Write the names of the animals. Colour them.**

_ o _ _ _ _ y   _ ion

_ _ eph _ _ _ _   _ a _ e _

C **Choose the correct word.**

1. Monkeys like _____ . (sweets, bananas, chips)

2. The elephant has a _____ . (bunk, train, trunk)

3. The camel has a _____ . (lump, bump, hump)

4. The giraffe has a long _____ . (deck, neck, peck)

A **Read about the giant panda. Colour the picture.**

The Giant Panda

The giant panda lives in China. It has a large body and a round face. It has small ears and a black patch around each eye. Its coat is thick and waterproof.

The panda is a very good climber. Its strong colours help to hide it.

The panda has huge teeth. It has very strong jaws to eat bamboo which is very tough. It has to eat huge amounts of bamboo. It spends fourteen hours a day eating. The rest of the time is spent sleeping. It has no special sleeping place.

The panda cub is tiny. It leaves its mother when it is one and a half years old to live alone.

The panda is now very rare. It is protected in China because there are so few left.

A **Answer these questions.**

1. What country does the panda live in?

_____

2. What does the panda look like?

_____

3. How long does the panda spend eating?

_____

4. What is a baby panda called?

_____

5. How long does a panda cub spend with its mother?

_____

6. The panda is very rare. What does this mean?

_____

B **Write yes or no.**

1. The giant panda lives in China. _____

2. The giant panda is thin. _____

3. The giant panda has a black patch around
one eye. _____

4. The giant panda is a poor climber. _____

5. The giant panda eats a lot of bamboo. _____

6. The giant panda spends little time eating. _____

7. The giant panda sleeps for about ten hours. _____

8. Giant panda cubs are tiny. _____

9. The giant panda can be found everywhere. _____

Ring the correct word.

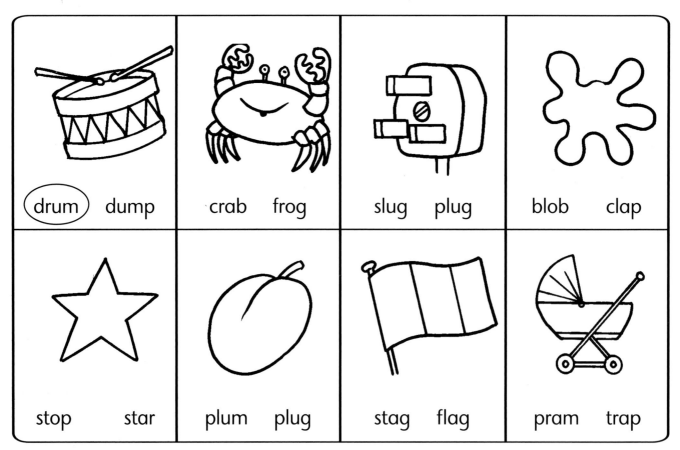

(drum) dump	crab frog	slug plug	blob clap
stop star	plum plug	stag flag	pram trap

 Write the correct missing letters.

lk   sk   st   nt   mp   rk   lt   sp

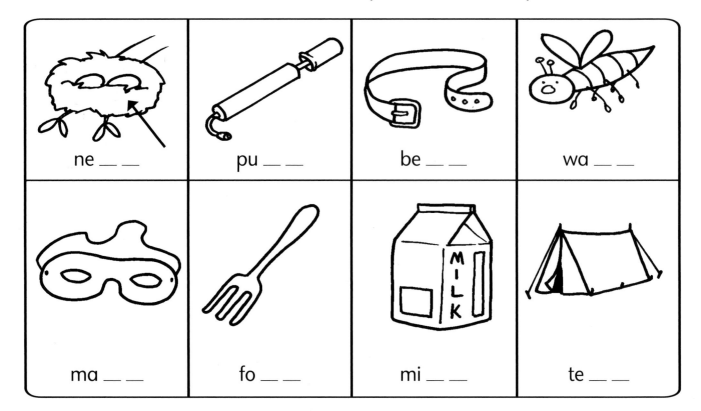

ne __ __	pu __ __	be __ __	wa __ __
ma __ __	fo __ __	mi __ __	te __ __

We put a full stop at the end of a sentence.
Example: Jack ran away from the giant.

 A Write these sentences correctly.
Do not forget capital letters.

1. tom is the fastest runner in our school

_____

2. goldilocks ate the porridge

_____

3. meg will be eight in august

_____

4. cinderella lost her slipper

_____

5. ben and i went to the park

_____

6. i lived in france for two years

_____

 B Unscramble these sentences. Do not
forget capital letters and full stops!

1. the fell leaves from trees the

_____

2. was she hungry and thirsty

_____

3. and jack jill up went the hill

_____

4. dumpty humpty on sat wall the

_____

Writing

 A **Write two sentences for each picture. Use the help words.**

A Close Call

	children park football kick
	1. _____
	_____
	2. _____
	_____

	hit fence road bounced
	1. _____
	_____
	2. _____
	_____

	ran after across car
	1. _____
	_____
	2. _____
	_____

	driver brakes skidded missed
	1. _____
	_____
	2. _____
	_____

A **Write to, too or two.**

Examples: I have two sweets.
I have to get a new copy.
Pat went home and Ann went too.

1. I have _____ hands and _____ feet.

2. I have _____ go _____ the shop.

3. Jin-Ho is sick and Shin is _____ .

4. May I have _____ apples?

5. I am going swimming _____ .

6. We want _____ eat.

B **Choose the missing words.**

jaws	teeth	waterproof	coat		face
body	China	panda		protected	rare
half	year	tiny		sleeping	fourteen

The giant _____ lives in _____ . It has a large

_____ and a round _____ . Its _____ is thick

and _____ . The panda has huge _____ and very

strong _____ . It spends _____ hours a day

eating and spends the rest of the day

_____ . Panda cubs are _____

and stay with their mothers for a

_____ and a _____ .

The panda is now very _____

and is _____ in China.

Read the story. Colour the picture.

The Goose that Laid the Golden Eggs

Once an old man and an old woman had a goose. It was a very special goose. Every day it laid a golden egg.

The old man and the old woman sold the eggs for lots of money. However, the more money they had the more they wanted.

They said, "If our goose lays golden eggs she must be made of gold. Let us cut her open and get out all the gold. Then we will have more money."

They killed the goose and cut her open. Then they found that she was just like any other goose. They found no gold inside. They had killed the goose so there were no more golden eggs. They did not get any more money.

In the end they had nothing.

A **Answer these questions.**

1. Who had a goose?

_____

2. Why was the goose special?

_____

3. What did the man and woman do with the eggs?

_____

4. Why did the man and woman kill the goose?

_____

5. What did they find inside the goose?

_____

6. Did they get any more golden eggs?

_____

7. Did they get any more money?

_____

8. What did they get in the end?

_____

B **Choose the correct word.**

1. The man and woman were _____. (young, middle-aged, old)

2. The couple had a _____. (duck, swan, goose)

3. A goose is a _____. (fish, bird, insect)

4. A goose has _____ (two, four, six) legs.

5. A goose has a covering of _____. (scales, fur, feathers)

6. The eggs were made of _____. (silver, gold, metal)

7. The eggs were sold for _____. (food, money, clothes)

8. The couple were _____. (kind, selfish, greedy)

Consonant Digraphs

shark

children

A | Write the missing letters: ch or sh.

__ __ ildren	__ __ ed	__ __ oot	__ __ ips
__ __ icken	__ __ eet	__ __ est	__ __ op
__ __ adow	__ __ op	__ __ elf	__ __ elter
__ __ urch	__ __ ip	__ __ air	__ __ in

B | Draw pictures for these words. Write the missing letters.

__ __ out	__ __ ell	__ __ ick	__ __ eese

English Skills 2

We use a question mark if the sentence asks a question.
Examples: Where? What? Who? Why? When? How?

A Add a question mark to each sentence. Answer the questions.

1. Where do you live _____

2. What is your name _____

3. Do you have a sister _____

4. Do you have a pet _____

5. How old are you _____

B Write the correct 'question' word. Add question marks.

How   What   When   Why   Is   Where   Does   Who

1. _____ your mum know you are here

2. _____ is your sick goldfish

3. _____ time is your bus due

4. _____ is your homework

5. _____ do you think you are trying to fool

6. _____ did you do that

7. _____ that the way you behave at home

8. _____ did your cat get better

C Write questions for these answers.

1. _____ Ali's birthday is in October.

2. _____ A swallow is a bird.

3. _____ April has 30 days.

4. _____ A spider has eight legs.

Writing

 Write two sentences for each picture. Use the help words.

The Merman

	princess fishing sea boat **1.** _____ _____ **2.** _____ _____
	caught merman line **1.** _____ _____ **2.** _____ _____
	changed prince handsome **1.** _____ _____ **2.** _____ _____
	married happily lived **1.** _____ _____ **2.** _____ _____

A Choose the correct 'opposite'.

sweet	slow	fresh	noisy
bright	empty	heavy	false

1. An orange can be bitter or _____ .

2. A bag can be light or _____ .

3. A train can be fast or _____ .

4. A bottle can be full or _____ .

5. A loaf of bread can be stale or _____ .

6. Children can be quiet or _____ .

7. Something we write can be true or _____ .

8. The day can be dull or _____ .

B Choose the correct word.

zoo	hive	hospital	garage
wardrobe	cinema	barracks	library

1. Soldiers live in a _____ .

2. Bees live in a _____ .

3. Cars are kept in a _____ .

4. Films are shown in a _____ .

5. Sick people go to a _____ .

6. Books are kept in a _____ .

7. We hang our clothes in a _____ .

8. Wild animals can be seen in a _____ .

Read the story. Colour the picture.

Who Can Jump the Highest?

The flea, the grasshopper and the frog met at the pond. They wanted to find out which one of them could jump the highest. They decided to have a competition. The king, his daughter and lots of people came. "I will give my daughter to the one who jumps the highest," said the king.

The flea jumped first. He jumped so high that no one could see where he had gone. Some people said that he had not jumped at all. Next came the grasshopper. He only jumped half as high, but jumped right into the king's face! The king was very angry. He thought that the grasshopper was very rude.

The frog was the last to jump. He stood so still that people thought he wasn't going to jump at all. Suddenly, he jumped into the arms of the princess.

"There is nothing higher than my daughter," said the king. "So the frog shall have her as his wife."

English Skills 2

A **Answer these questions.**

1. Where did the flea, the grasshopper and the frog meet?

_____

2. What did the flea, the grasshopper and the frog want to find out?

3. What did the king say? _____

4. Who jumped first? _____

5. What did the grasshopper do? _____

6. What did the king think of the grasshopper? _____

7. Who was the last to jump? _____

8. Do you think the princess was happy to marry a frog? _____

_____

B **Choose the correct word.**

1. The flea jumped _____ (last, second, first).

2. The king thought the grasshopper was _____ (nice, cheeky, rude).

3. The frog stood _____ (up, still, behind).

4. People _____ (love, like, hate) fleas.

5. The _____ (grasshopper, flea, frog) really jumped the highest.

6. The frog was _____ (silly, clever, stupid).

A **Read each word. Add a 'magic e'. Read each word again.**

cap___   can___   tap___   mat___   pan___

B **Unscramble these letters.**

1. ekab	_____	**6.** gaem	_____
2. egat	_____	**7.** afme	_____
3. kale	_____	**8.** emca	_____
4. meal	_____	**9.** adem	_____
5. etad	_____	**10.** ekra	_____

C **Write the missing letters.**

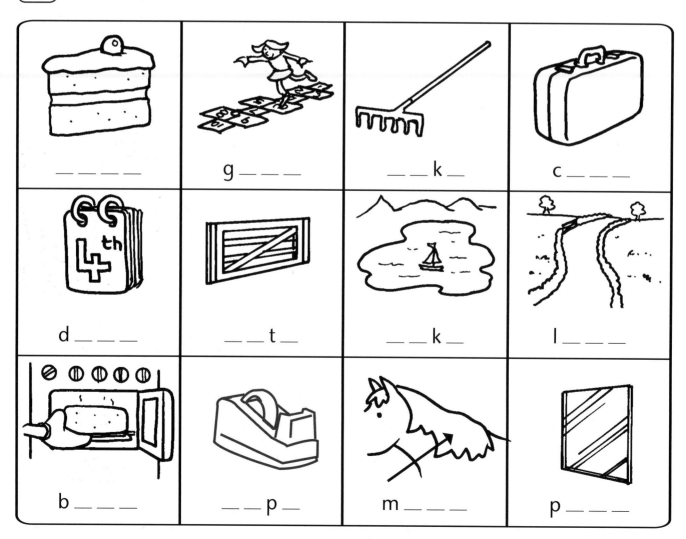

_ _ _ _   g _ _ _   _ _ k _   c _ _ _ _

d _ _ _   _ _ t _   _ _ k _   l _ _ _ _

b _ _ _ _   _ _ p _   m _ _ _   p _ _ _ _

Nouns

A noun is the name of a person, place or thing.
Examples: Tom, Asia, London, apple.

A **Ring the nouns.**

1. My name is Meg.

2. Granny is coming today.

3. Apples are good for you.

4. Ben and Tom are here.

5. The rabbit is afraid of the fox.

6. Erina is in Egypt.

7. The hen is laying an egg.

8. The bird is in the tree.

B **Write the correct noun.**

ball   tree   glass   bone   table   grass

1. The robin is in the _____ .

2. Sam kicked the _____ .

3. Sheep like to eat _____ .

4. The cup is on the _____ .

5. I drink water from a _____ .

6. The dog has a _____ .

C **Write the names of these nouns. Colour the pictures.**

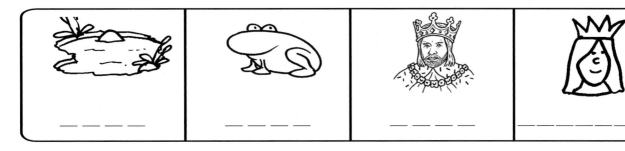

_ _ _ _   _ _ _ _   _ _ _ _   _ _ _ _ _ _ _ _

Writing

A **Write two sentences for each picture. Use the help words.**

	walking carrying bone
	1. _____
	_____
	2. _____
	_____
	bridge stream crossing
	1. _____
	_____
	2. _____
	_____
	himself water greedy
	1. _____
	_____
	2. _____
	_____
	opens drops nothing
	1. _____
	_____
	2. _____
	_____

A   Choose the 'odd one out'.

1. swan, swing, blue, swim, swap   _____

2. shop, sheep, ship, shell, brush   _____

3. skin, floor, sky, skirt, skip   _____

4. slow, clown, slip, sleep, slug   _____

5. sweets, swim, sweep, plum, swallow   _____

6. smoke, white, smile, smell, small   _____

7. spoon, spot, glass, spade, spy   _____

8. stick, story, stable, stamp, drum   _____

9. sharp, shed, shut, shape, fruit   _____

10. snow, snap, sleep, snack, snake   _____

B   Write right or write.

1. Do I turn _____ or left here?

2. Can I _____ to you?

3. The shop is _____ in the middle of town.

4. I _____ with my left hand.

5. It is not _____ to drop litter.

6. Will you _____ the date, please?

7. Turn _____ at the crossroads.

8. I will _____ a letter to you.

C   How many small words can you make from 'grasshopper'?

_____   _____   _____

_____   _____   _____

A **Read the story. Colour the picture.**

King of the Birds

One day, all the birds met in a large forest. There were owls, pigeons, cuckoos, blackbirds, sparrows, gulls, ducks, hawks – every kind of bird was there. Suddenly, a great eagle landed beside them. "I am the King of the Birds," said the eagle. "No other bird can fly faster than I."

All the birds were silent. Then a tiny wren spoke up. "I can fly faster than you," he said quietly. The eagle laughed at this. They decided to have a race. The first bird to fly to the top of the highest mountain would be the King of the Birds. The race began and soon the eagle was well ahead of the little wren. In fact, he was so far ahead that he flew into a cloud for a rest and fell fast asleep.

Up, up and up into the sky flew the brave, little wren. Suddenly, he came to the cloud where the eagle was sleeping. The poor wren was so tired that he could fly no further. He flew into the cloud and landed quietly on the eagle's back. The eagle's great feathers were soft and warm. "I think I'll have a short sleep," said the wren.

When the eagle awoke, he never felt the tiny wren asleep on his back. Flapping his wide wings, he hurried away. Hours later, the eagle saw the top of the highest mountain ahead of him. Suddenly, the wren awoke. He leapt up into the air, flew past the tired eagle and straight onto the top of the highest mountain. The wren was the winner and became the King of the Birds.

Answer these questions.

1. Where did the birds meet?

_____

2. What landed beside them?

_____

3. Which bird said he could fly faster than the eagle?

_____

4. Where was the race to finish?

_____

5. Where did the eagle stop for a rest?

_____

6. Who won the race?

_____

 Write the names of the birds. Colour the pictures.

_ _ _ r _ _ _ _   _ _ ck _ _ _   _ _ _ _ eo _

_ _ _ ck _ i _ _   _ _ _ _ le   wr _ _ _

A Read each word. Add a 'magic e'. Read each word again.

pip ___   rip ___   fin ___   rid ___   fir ___

B Write the correct word.

pale pipe	like hike	ride rice	wire wide
_____	_____	_____	_____
broke bike	tame time	fine fire	hide hive
_____	_____	_____	_____
pane pine	mine mane	tile tale	hike kite
_____	_____	_____	_____

C Unscramble these letters.

1. etib _____   **6.** enif _____

2. ecir _____   **7.** ekil _____

3. edir _____   **8.** elim _____

4. epir _____   **9.** ecid _____

5. enip _____   **10.** enim _____

Nouns

A **Write each noun in the correct list.**

Meg   apple   Cairo   pencil   Ben   Madras
Dubai   Tom   book   Erina   doll   Spain

Person	Place	Thing
_____	_____	_____
_____	_____	_____
_____	_____	_____
_____	_____	_____

B **Choose the correct noun.**

hedgehog   hammer   bed   monkey   fox   pond

1. The crow drank water from the _____ .

2. The _____ ran after the rabbit.

3. The _____ slept for the winter.

4. The _____ ate twenty bananas.

5. I hit the nail with a _____ .

6. The queen put peas on the _____ .

C **Write your own list of nouns.**

Person	Place	Thing
_____	_____	_____
_____	_____	_____
_____	_____	_____
_____	_____	_____

Write two sentences for each picture. Use the help words.

The Shopping Trip

man   baker   bread

1. _____

_____

2. _____

_____

bicycle   road   basket

1. _____

_____

2. _____

_____

birds   followed   pecked

1. _____

_____

2. _____

_____

home   empty   surprised

1. _____

_____

2. _____

_____

A Choose the 'odd one out'.

1. teacher, Ann, nurse, doctor _____

2. yellow, blue, green, sky _____

3. apple, pear, turnip, plum _____

4. skirt, dress, leg, hat _____

5. piano, violin, wood, drum _____

6. glass, table, cup, jug _____

7. elephant, tiger, giraffe, goose _____

8. rose, daffodil, carrot, snowdrop _____

B Choose the missing words.

asleep	back	woke	on	jumped	won	line
cloud	front	race	King	wren	eagle	forest

One day all the birds met in the f_____ . The e_____ said that

he was King of the Birds. The w_____ said that he was the

K_____ of the Birds. They decided to have a r_____ .

The eagle was in f_____ of the wren. He decided to stop for a rest in a c

_____ but he fell a_____ . The wren

saw the eagle and landed on his b_____ .

The eagle w_____ up and flew on.

He didn't know the wren was _____ his

back. When they got to the finishing

l_____ the wren j_____ off the

eagle's back. He flew past the eagle

and w_____ the race.

A **Read about the ladybird. Colour the pictures.**

The Ladybird

1

This ladybird is laying eggs. She lays them on a plant covered in greenfly.

2

The eggs hatch out. Dark grubs creep out of each egg. Each grub has six legs. They eat the greenfly.

3

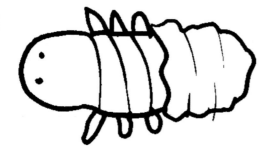

The grubs eat and eat until their skins burst. They creep out of the old skins.

4

Now the grubs have grey-blue skin. They eat again until they are full. They hang upside down. Their skins burst. Each grub has become a chrysalis.

5

One week later, a yellow ladybird creeps out. After a while it gets its red colour and seven black spots.

6

The ladybird flies away to look for food. It is very hungry because it could not eat when it was a chrysalis.

7

A frog catches the ladybird. The ladybird squirts a horrible yellow liquid at the frog. The frog drops the ladybird.

8

It is autumn. The ladybird finds a crack in the bark of an apple tree. It creeps inside with another ladybird and goes to sleep.

Activities

 Answer these questions.

1. Where does the ladybird lay her eggs?

_____

2. What creeps out of each egg?

_____

3. How many legs has a grub?

_____

4. What creeps out of the chrysalis?

_____

5. What does the ladybird do to the frog?

_____

6. What does the ladybird do in autumn?

_____

B **Try this wordsearch.**

ladybird

eggs

greenfly

grubs

skin

chrysalis

frog

squirt

liquid

autumn

c	h	r	y	s	a	l	i	s
g	r	u	b	s	b	d	l	a
r	f	b	c	q	e	c	a	u
e	g	w	m	u	k	v	d	t
e	x	h	t	i	j	u	y	u
n	n	o	s	r	l	y	b	m
f	r	o	g	t	s	k	i	n
l	l	i	q	u	i	d	r	z
y	r	p	e	g	g	s	d	c

Magic E

A Read each word. Add a 'magic e'. Read each word again.

rob ____   cod ____   cop ____   rod ____

B Write the correct word.

pole poke	core cone	mole pole	hole hose
____	____	____	____
code core	cone bone	nose rose	hole home
____	____	____	____
rode robe	hole hope	rose rope	sole note
____	____	____	____

C Choose the correct word.

1. The king will _____ (dune, rule, pure) for six years.

2. She is humming a very nice _____ (time, tune, tame).

3. He _____ (rode, robe, rude) the horse into town.

4. There is no _____ (cube, cure, core) for that illness.

5. I can see a _____ (tube, tune, tide) of toothpaste.

6. She is a very _____ (rude, ride, tide) girl.

> **'Doing words' are called verbs.**
> **Examples: walk, run, fall, talk.**

 Choose the correct verb.

run   walk   talk   read   eat   drink   play   swim

p l a y   ___   ___   ___

___   ___   ___   ___

 Ring the verbs.

1. Tom (fell) off the wall.

2. The girl ran very fast.

3. Hanah read the book.

4. Ben cut the paper.

5. Sujit swims on Monday.

6. I drink milk every day.

A **Write two sentences for each picture. Use the help words.**

Cat Rescue

	noticed trapped roof 1. _____ _____ 2. _____ _____
	telephoned fire brigade told 1. _____ _____ 2. _____ _____
	arrived fire engine ladder 1. _____ _____ 2. _____ _____
	climbed rescued brought 1. _____ _____ 2. _____ _____

Activities

A Write the lists below in order of size (the biggest first).

1. lamb, cat, person, horse _____

2. pumpkin, pea, turnip, tomato _____

3. pigeon, eagle, wren, robin _____

4. stag, fox, rabbit, hedgehog _____

5. apple, grape, melon, kiwi _____

6. boy, man, baby, teenager _____

7. tiger, elephant, zebra, monkey _____

B Choose the correct verb.

crashed   swam   galloped   hopped
flew   opened   fell   blew

1. A plane _____ .

2. The fish _____ .

3. The horse _____ .

4. The frog _____ .

5. A wind _____ .

6. The butterfly _____ .

7. Snow _____ .

8. The door _____ .

C Choose the correct word.

1. A cat has a coat of _____ . (wool, fur, feathers)

2. A cat is an _____ . (bird, animal, insect)

3. A cat likes to eat _____ . (corn, fish, snails)

4. A young cat is called a _____ . (cub, pup, kitten)

5. A cat likes to chase _____ . (mice, dogs, cows)

6. A happy cat _____ . (barks, purrs, roars)

7. A cat has a long _____ . (nose, tail, ear)

8. A cat has no _____ . (horns, whiskers, tail)

A **Read about the frog. Colour the pictures.**

The Frog

1

At first, frogs' eggs look like tiny, black dots inside balls of jelly.

2

Soon the black dots grow bigger and become baby tadpoles. The tadpoles eat the jelly and wriggle out to get more food. The tiny tadpoles love to eat water weeds.

3

The tadpole has gills so that it can get air from the water. It looks like all head and tail until its legs begin to grow.

4

The back legs come first. They grow strong and long so that the frog can jump.

5

Soon the gills are gone and the front legs begin to grow. The tail gets shorter and shorter until there is none left. The young frog has used it up for food.

6

From now on, the frog must hunt bugs for its dinner!

Answer these questions.

1. What are the 'tiny, black dots'?

_____

2. What do tadpoles eat?

_____

3. Why does the tadpole have gills?

_____

4. Which legs grow first?

_____

5. What happens to the tadpole's tail?

_____

6. What will the young frogs eat?

_____

B **Choose the correct word.**

1. Frogs' eggs look like black _____. (tops, dots, pots)

2. Tadpoles eat the _____. (belly, telly, jelly)

3. The tadpole has _____. (bills, gills, gulls)

4. The tadpole's _____ (back, front, frost) legs grow first.

5. The tadpole loses its _____. (tale, nail, tail)

6. The frog eats _____. (flies, flowers, flags)

C **Write yes or no.**

1. Frogs' eggs look like tiny, brown dots. _____

2. Soon the black dots become baby tadpoles. _____

3. The tadpole has no gills. _____

4. The young frog uses its tail for food. _____

A **Try this 'magic e' crossword.**

Across

1. A dog would like one.
4. It comes in and goes out again.
6. It is used in the garden.
7. Give and _____ .
9. The bread is not fresh.
11. You are singing out of _____ .
14. Horses and ponies have one.
16. It is full of water, fish and plants.
17. It rhymes with mice.
19. If it's not wild it must be _____ .
20. It has thirty days.
21. It is like a small rock.

Down

2. You bring one if you are late.
3. Give some to other people.
5. You will find one on the calendar.
8. You can fly it on a windy day.
10. You might see one on the beach. It rhymes with tune.
12. Everyone has one but most people like their own.
13. You might find one in a classroom. It spins around.
15. 4 + 5 = this number.
16. A green fruit like a lemon.
18. You get one on your birthday.
20. A short, funny story.

Grammar

 Write the correct verb.

write   cry   laugh   paint   jump   hop   sing   bark

l a u g h   _ _ _ _ _   _ _ _ _ _   _ _ _ _ _

_ _ _ _   _ _ _ _ _   _ _ _ _ _   _ _ _ _ _

 Ring each verb then write it.

1. Tom   dog   (sing)   tree   _____sing_____

2. cat   Emma   frog   hop   _____

3. baby   run   milk   ball   _____

4. rabbit   Sam   look   tea   _____

5. fox   Ben   pen   fall   _____

6. swim   teddy   book   Meg   _____

A **Write two sentences for each picture. Use the help words.**

The Treasure Chest

pirates   ship   map

1. _____

_____

2. _____

_____

island   beach   coconuts

1. _____

_____

2. _____

_____

looking   treasure   find

1. _____

_____

2. _____

_____

chest   open   crabs

1. _____

_____

2. _____

_____

Activities

A Choose the correct word.

1. A frog _____. (roars, barks, croaks)

2. A frog eats _____. (nuts, insects, fruit)

3. A frog has webbed _____. (ears, eyes, feet)

4. A frog is bigger than a _____. (flea, person, sheep)

5. A frog can _____. (fly, swim, talk)

6. A young frog is called a _____. (toad, caterpillar, tadpole)

7. An adult frog has no _____. (eyes, tail, skin)

8. A frog loves to eat _____. (mice, chicks, flies)

B Choose the missing word.

foal   kid   cub   puppy   leveret   kitten

1. A young hare is called a _____ .

2. A young dog is called a _____ .

3. A young cat is called a _____ .

4. A young tiger is called a _____ .

5. A young horse is called a _____ .

6. A young goat is called a _____ .

C Choose the correct word.

1. Another word for little is _____. (large, small, fat, huge)

2. Another word for nice is _____. (thin, ugly, kind, rough)

3. Another word for difficult is _____. (easy, fine, nice, hard)

4. Another word for large is _____. (lean, small, tiny, big)

5. Another word for start is _____. (end, stop, begin, finish)

A **Read the story. Colour the picture.**

The Little White Cat

A giant lived in a great castle with a hundred doors. Each door was guarded by a huge dog. The giant hated the King of Ireland who was richer than he was! One day he kidnapped Prince Conor, the king's son, and locked him in a tower in the castle.

The prince could not escape from the high tower. The king and his men were afraid to come near the castle to help him. One morning, the prince saw a little, white cat on a branch just outside his window. He told the cat his sad story. "I will help you," said the cat.

The cat ran until it came to the Palace of the Silver River. A princess called Diana lived there. The cat told her about the prince. Diana promised to help free the prince from the cruel giant. Before she left, she baked a hundred magic cakes and made a net of magic wool.

Then she got on her white horse and raced towards the castle with the white cat behind her. When the princess reached the giant's castle, the hungry dogs rushed out to eat her. She fed them with the magic cakes. Each dog fell fast asleep the moment it ate one of the cakes.

Princess Diana was now able to enter the giant's castle. She went in the door and made her way up the stairs to the tower. The giant heard her footsteps and came rushing down. "Who dares to come to my castle?" he roared.

The little, white cat was so frightened that it ran back down the stairs, but Diana waited. When the cruel giant came near, she threw the magic net over his head. Even a strong giant could not free himself from this net. Prince Conor was free at last!

Activities

A **Answer these questions.**

1. Why did the giant kidnap the prince?

_____

2. Why did the king not rescue the prince?

_____

3. Who lived at the Palace of the Silver River?

_____

4. What did the princess give the dogs?

_____

5. Why did the white cat run back down the stairs?

_____

6. What do you think Prince Conor said to the princess?

_____

B **Choose the correct word.**

1. The giant _____ (killed, kissed, kidnapped) the prince.

2. The princess _____ (hated, baked, burnt) cakes.

3. The dogs _____ (eight, ate, ape) the cakes.

4. The giant _____ (rained, roared, roasted).

5. The _____ (cat, dog, prince) ran back down the stairs.

6. The princess _____ (through, threw, true) the net.

C **Write yes or no.**

1. The giant locked the king in a tower. _____

2. The prince saw a little, black cat. _____

3. The cat went to the Palace of the Golden River. _____

4. The princess fed the dogs with magic cakes. _____

Vowel Digraphs

A Write the correct 'oa' word.

soap goat	goat boat	road soap	coal goal
_____	_____	_____	_____
coat coal	oak oats	loan load	toast toad
_____	_____	_____	_____
toad oats	foal float	goal coal	goat goal
_____	_____	_____	_____

B Write the missing letters in these 'ai' words.

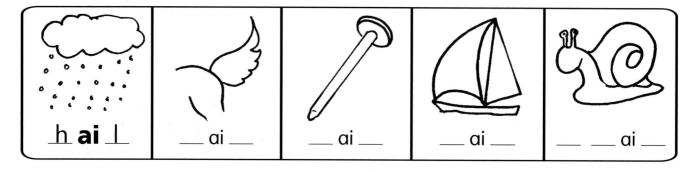

h **ai** l   __ ai __   __ ai __   __ ai __   __ __ ai __

C Choose the correct word.

1. I am going to _____ (sale, sail, soil, salt) my boat.

2. I hurt my hand and the _____ (pain, pan, pane, pine) is awful.

3. I want to get my _____ (hare, hail, hair, rare) cut short.

4. I cannot _____ (wait, waist, wave, wire) for the holidays.

A The nouns and verbs have got mixed up.
Write them in the correct 'jar' below.

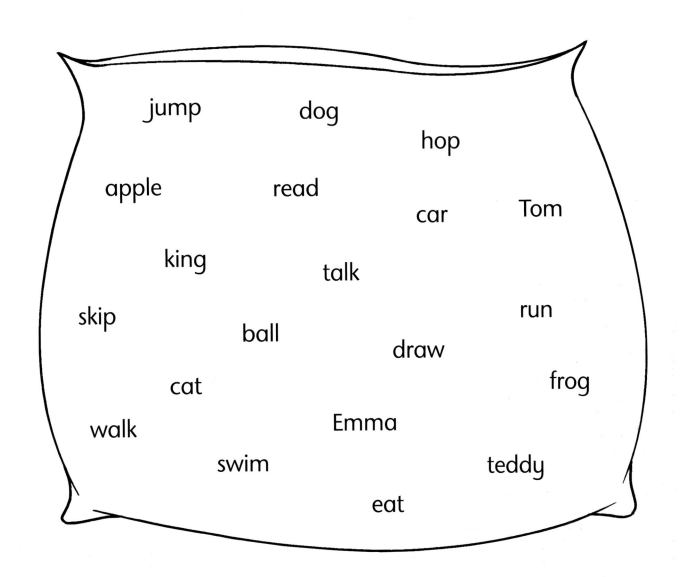

jump   dog   hop   apple   read   car   Tom   king   talk   skip   run   ball   draw   cat   frog   walk   Emma   swim   teddy   eat

Nouns

Emma _____ _____

_____ _____

_____ _____

_____ _____

_____

Verbs

jump _____ _____

_____ _____

_____ _____

_____ _____

A **Write two sentences for each picture. Use the help words.**

Picnic at the Beach

	sunny beach raced 1. _____ _____ 2. _____ _____
	sandcastle spades rested sunbed 1. _____ _____ 2. _____ _____
	swim crab pinched fright 1. _____ _____ 2. _____ _____
	rug picnic sandwiches drinks 1. _____ _____ 2. _____ _____

A **Choose the correct word.**

swarm   litter   nest   herd   pack   brood   flock   shoal

1. A _____ of elephants.

2. A _____ of pups.

3. A _____ of mice.

4. A _____ of wolves.

5. A _____ of bees.

6. A _____ of fish.

7. A _____ of birds.

8. A _____ of chickens.

B **Choose the correct 'opposite'.**

soft   big   wet   sweet   light   black   empty   stale

1. The blackberry is small but the apple is _____ .

2. The nut is hard but the peach is _____ .

3. The sand is dry but the water is _____ .

4. The lemon is bitter but the pear is _____ .

5. The coconut is heavy but the cherry is _____ .

6. The snow is white but the coal is _____ .

7. The lettuce is fresh but the bread is _____ .

8. The basket is full but the bag is _____ .

C **Choose the correct word.**

1. The _____ (pig, bear, tiger) has a long tail.

2. The _____ (horse, cat, rabbit) has a short tail.

3. The _____ (rabbit, mouse, squirrel) has a bushy tail.

4. The _____ (horse, deer, hare) has a long tail.

5. The _____ (lion, sheep, kangaroo) has a short tail.

6. The _____ (lamb, goat, fox) has a bushy tail.

A **Read about the koala. Colour the picture.**

The Koala

Koalas live in Australia. People sometimes call them 'koala bears' but they are not related to bears at all. Koalas have grey fur, with a white chin and chest. Their ears are fringed with white fur and they have a large, leathery nose. They have strong, sharp claws for climbing. They have almost no tail.

Koalas live in forests of eucalyptus trees. Their favourite food is eucalyptus leaves, but sometimes they eat leaves from other trees and bushes. Koalas do not need to come down from the trees to find water. They get all the water they need from their food. In fact, the word 'koala' means 'no drink' in the language of the Aborigines.

Koalas sleep for up to twenty hours a day. Koalas are solitary, which means they live alone. Koalas do not sweat to keep cool. Instead, they cool themselves by licking their arms.

After they are born, baby koalas spend seven months in their mother's pouch. After that, they spend five months clinging to their mother's back. Even after they have left their mother's back, young koalas live near their mother for some time.

A **Answer these questions.**

1. Where do koalas live?

_____

2. What sort of a tail do koalas have?

_____

3. What is the koala's favourite food?

_____

4. What does the word 'koala' mean?

_____

5. How many hours a day can koalas spend asleep?

_____

6. How long do koalas spend in their mother's pouch?

_____

 B **Fill in the missing letters. Colour the pictures.**

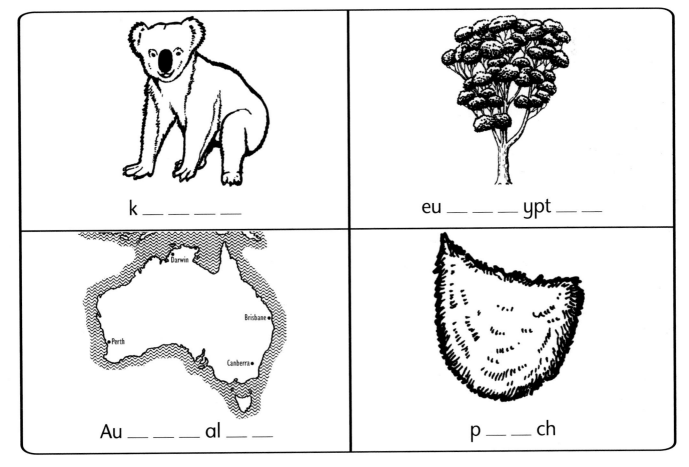

k _ _ _ _ _

eu _ _ _ ypt _ _

Au _ _ _ al _ _

p _ _ ch

Find these 'oo' words.

fool
roof
tool
cool
cook
food
moon
zoo
boot
pool
spoon
shoot
broom

d	s	r	j	k	f	w	p	s	p	o	o	n	d	e
q	k	r	c	x	w	y	b	n	g	f	l	d	s	b
v	c	e	w	s	l	h	g	c	x	s	o	y	t	a
l	v	g	r	o	o	f	s	a	n	o	h	l	r	l
m	o	o	n	f	c	o	s	l	h	x	t	o	d	l
c	u	o	e	f	x	o	e	s	z	x	z	o	o	o
u	b	g	t	o	o	l	x	f	r	z	a	n	r	o
y	p	w	r	o	f	g	y	r	e	x	l	y	b	n
w	u	g	b	d	a	b	r	o	o	m	s	g	t	v
a	p	o	o	l	f	t	r	s	b	o	o	t	r	s
h	i	d	o	s	r	s	b	h	p	r	d	x	k	h
g	s	o	c	m	j	s	p	a	q	s	h	o	o	t
q	c	o	o	k	u	i	i	o	t	d	v	i	p	k
b	r	v	h	j	p	i	m	d	o	d	e	w	q	i

B **Write a sentence for each 'ew' word.**

1. new _____

2. few _____

3. flew _____

4. stew _____

5. grew _____

6. chew _____

7. crew _____

8. drew _____

English Skills 2

A **Write these sentences correctly. Do not forget capital letters and full stops!**

1. we have fish on mondays

_____

2. ben and i are going to cape town

_____

3. i am having a party in june

_____

4. jack and tom went to london

_____

B **Ring each verb then write it.**

1. Aba	duck	(sit)	car		_____sit_____
2. bag	Kim	bird	run		_____
3. draw	apple	Maha	grass		_____
4. poppy	pick	bee	tree		_____
5. sleep	box	bed	Sam		_____
6. pond	Rajan	walk	table		_____

C **Write the correct noun under each picture.**

duck   ring   horse   tent   baby   ball

_____	_____	_____
_____	_____	_____

A **Ring the two short words in these words. Write them.**

1. (gold)(fish) = _____gold_____ + _____fish_____

2. matchstick = _____ + _____

3. tightrope = _____ + _____

4. seasick = _____ + _____

5. blackberry = _____ + _____

6. shipwreck = _____ + _____

7. toothbrush = _____ + _____

8. rattlesnake = _____ + _____

9. waterfall = _____ + _____

10. skateboard = _____ + _____

B **Choose the correct word.**

1. The bird _____ (walks, flies, hops) over the water.

2. The eagle _____ (swims, swings, swoops) on its prey.

3. The butterfly _____ (hovers, runs, trots) over the flower.

4. The duck _____ (waddles, gallops, leaps) into the pond.

C **How many short words can you make from 'caterpillar'?**

_____   _____   _____

_____   _____   _____

_____   _____   _____

_____   _____   _____

English Skills 2